INTRODUCTION
2

BEFORE YOU BEGIN THE EXERCISES

Breathing for T'ai-chi Ch'uan

Practice this kind of breathing separately at first; then when it becomes natural, incorporate it into the exercises. Inhale deeply, placing the tip of your tongue behind the front teeth. When exhaling, return the tongue to its normal position. Take about 4 breaths a minute (16 seconds for each).

→ Inhale (about 8 seconds)   **⇨** Exhale (about 8 seconds)

Due to the complexity of some movements, the length of the arrows is sometimes different. However, always take 8 seconds for each of the 2 arrows. "Slowness, lightness and quietness": these 3 words characterize T'ai-chi Ch'uan. Please keep them in mind as you perform the exercises.

BEFORE YOU BEGIN THE EXERCISES
4

Standing Zen
立 禪
Lieh Chan

This exercise prepares the mind for the 8 exercises. Always practice it before beginning the series. Stand with your feet spread apart to shoulder width and concentrate your mind upon the abdomen. Bend your knees slightly and hold your shoulders and arms naturally. Use the T'ai-chi Ch'uan breathing method, and close your eyes slightly. You will find worldly thoughts disappearing from your mind; you will recover from fatigue and feel calm. (In the beginning if you cannot take long breaths, you may breathe naturally.)

無我　　　　　　　　　　　　　　　　　　　　　　　　無心

氣

沈肩　　　　　　　　　　　　　　　　　　　　　　　　垂肘

BEFORE YOU BEGIN THE EXERCISES

Swinging Hands

甩 手

Sowai Shou

After you finish standing *zen,* swing your both arms right and left like a pendulum. Relax your shoulders, and turn your torso gently. Do not swing your arms strongly. Repeat this movement for several minutes until your shoulders feel relaxed.

Note: Always do these exercises in order whether you do the whole series or only a few. And always **finish** with standing *zen* and swinging hands as you did when starting.

You can practice each exercise as many times as you like. What is important is to keep practicing every day.

EXERCISE I
Suang Shou Tou Tien Li San Ziao
双手托天理三焦

Purpose: To improve digestion and strengthen abdominal muscles.

Points:
    (1) Stand naturally. Relax shoulders and elbows, and try to keep your breathing rhythmical. Then fold your hands in front of your waist.

    (2) Raise your hands slowly and stop them at shoulder-height.

    (3-4) Lower hands to abdomen.

EXERCISE I

10

Fold your hands.

(5-6) Raise hands above your head, and stretch them.

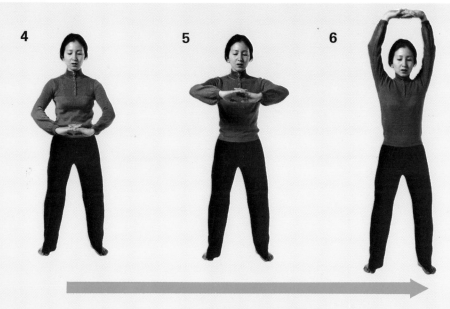

EXERCISE I

12

(7-8) Bring your hands down in a circle.

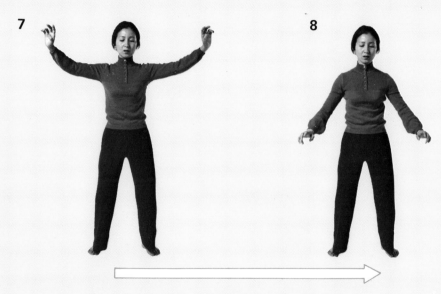

EXERCISE I

14

EXERCISE II
Tso Yu Kai Kung Ssu Shê Jao
左右開弓似射雕

Purpose: To reduce and improve the line of arms and shoulders, chest, and bust. Blood circulation is increased, and so fatigue is reduced.

Points: (A) Start with **half sitting posture.** Separate feet widely and bend a little, keeping body straight. This posture strengthens the knees. (If you feel pain, stand naturally.)

(1-3) Hold hands in front of body with elbows bent a little. Raise arms to chest.

EXERCISE II
16

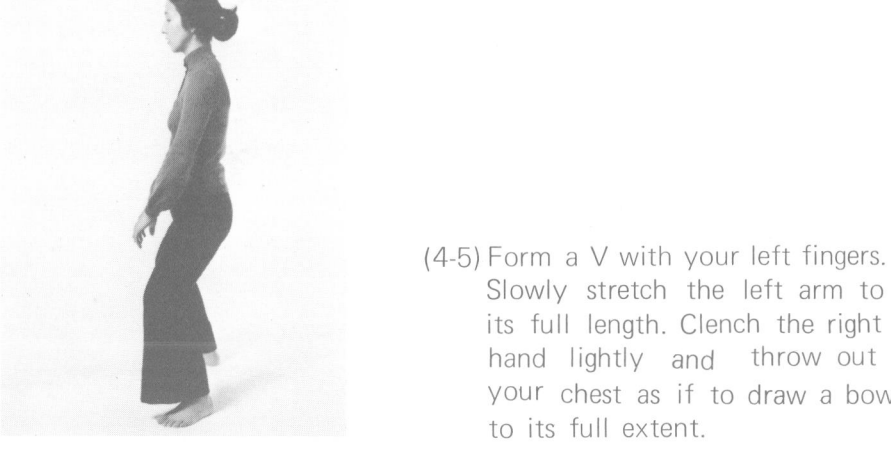

A

(4-5) Form a V with your left fingers. Slowly stretch the left arm to its full length. Clench the right hand lightly and throw out your chest as if to draw a bow to its full extent.

4

5

EXERCISE II
18

Form a V.

(6-7) Slowly bring back your left hand.
(8) Put both hands down to starting position. Repeat with your right hand.

EXERCISE II
20

EXERCISE III
Tiao Li Pi Wei Shu Tan Chu
調理脾胃須單舉

Purpose: To improve digestion and help those who suffer from ulcers. Good for the arms and shoulders.

Points: (1) Stand naturally.

(2) Turn palms up and raise arms.

1   2

EXERCISE III
22

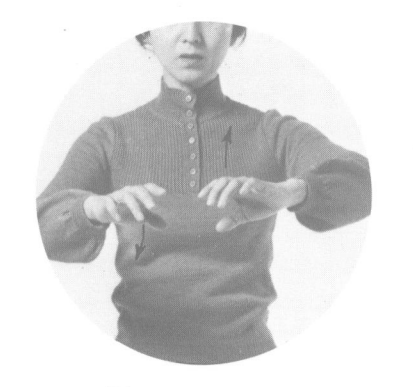

Turn palms down.
Raise your left hand and
lower your right hand slowly.

(3) At shoulder level turn palms down, bend elbows, and bring hands to chest.
(4-5) Then raise your left hand in a circular motion, and lower your right hand. When your left hand reaches above your head, stop your breath.

3   **4**   **5**

EXERCISE III

24

(6-8) Bring your left hand down. Repeat with your right hand.

EXERCISE IV
Wu Lao Chi Shang Wang Hou Chiao
五勞七傷往后瞧

Purpose: To invigorate through quiet action. Very good for conva-
lescents.

Points: (1-2) Raise your arms as you did in Exercise 3. Concentrate
your mind upon your abdomen. Relax your shoulders.
If you are not relaxed, you cannot move your body.

EXERCISE IV
28

Simultaneously turn your head to left.

(3-6) At shoulder level, turn palms down, lower the hands and simultaneously turn your head to left.

EXERCISE IV
30

EXERCISE IV

(7) Raise hands again and turn head to face front.
(8) When you are again facing forward, put your hands down. Repeat, turning to the right.

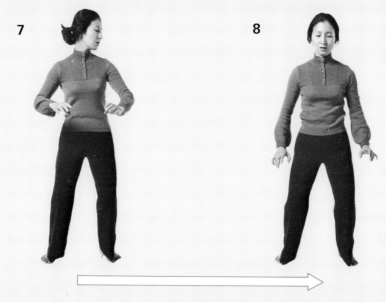

7　　　　　　　　　　　8

EXERCISE V
Yao Tou Pai Wei Chu Hsin Huo
搖頭擺尾去心火

Purpose: To reduce stress. Also to strengthen and smooth the leg muscles.

Points: **Keep back straight throughout this exercise.**

(1) Stand in **half sitting posture** with hands on thighs.

(2-3) Turn upper body to the right, twisting at the waist. The head should also turn in the direction of the body. The body leans forward. The thighs support the weight of the torso.

EXERCISE V
34

(4)   Keeping torso low, return to the center.
(5-6) Continue the same movement, this time to the left.

4 **5** **6**

(7-8) Return to the center and raise torso to starting position.

7 8

EXERCISE V
38

EXERCISE VI
Liang Shou Ban Tsu Ku Shion Yao
兩手攀足固腎腰

Purpose: To strengthen legs and relax muscles. Helps relieve consti-
pation.

Points: (1-2) Stand with knees slightly bent and your palms down.
(3-4) Raise hands above head and stretch your body.

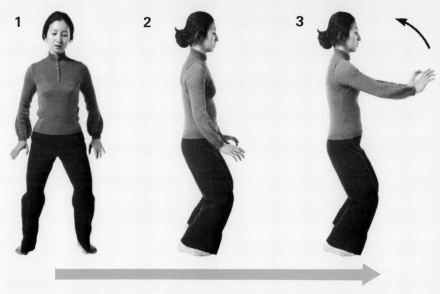

EXERCISE VI

40

Bend your body forward.

(5-8) Bend your body forward.

EXERCISE VI
42

(6) Straighten body.

8

9

EXERCISE VI

EXERCISE VII
Tsan Chuan Nu Mu Tsêng Chi Li
攢拳怒目增氣力

Make fists.

Purpose: A general reducing exercise; improves body proportions. Recommended for those with high blood pressure.

Points: (1) Stand in **half sitting posture.** (If you feel pain, stand naturally.)

(2-3) Make fists and raise them to chest level and extend the left fist diagonally forward.

EXERCISE VII

46

Extend the left fist.

(4-5) Bring it back.

4

5

6

(6-7) Then raise your both hands above your head.

7   8

EXERCISE VII
50

(8-10) Put your hands down, drawing a large circle.

EXERCISE VII
52

EXERCISE VIII
Pei Hou Chi Tien Pai Ping Hsiao
背后七顛百病消

Purpose: To strengthen legs and promote blood circulation. Especially recommended for those with hemorrhoids.

Points:
   (1) Stand erect with feet together, palms down and fingers extended and close together.

   (2-3) Slowly raise both heels. Hold the balance and raise them even higher. Concentrate your energy upon your abdomen so as to firmly close the anus.

   (4) Drop heels heavily back to floor, and relax muscles.

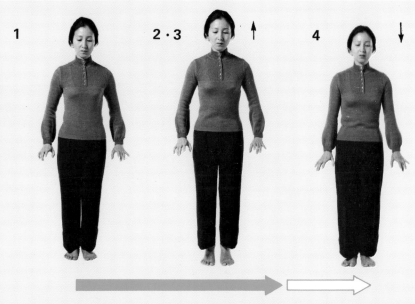

1   2 · 3 ↑   4 ↓

EXERCISE VIII
54

From Sideview.

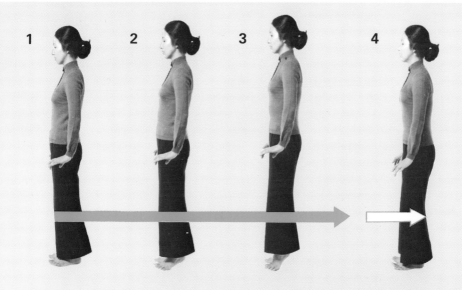

EXERCISE VIII
56

2

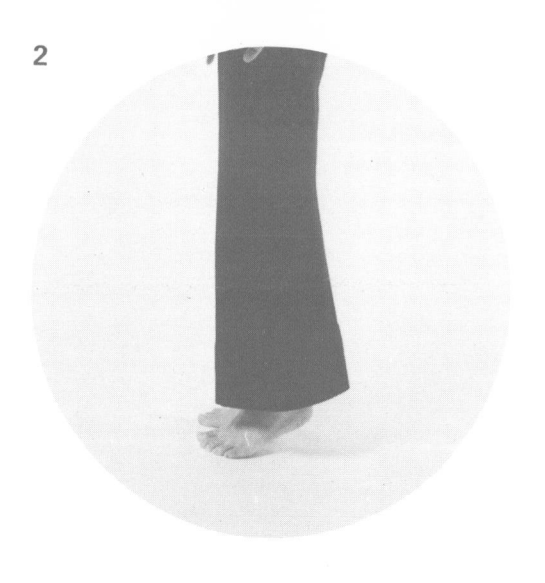

3

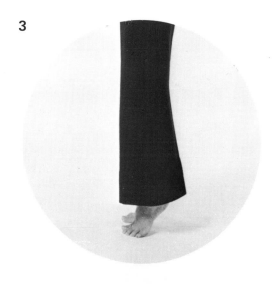

ABOUT THE AUTHOR

The author, **Mr. Yang Ming-shih,** was born in Wutai Prefecture of Shansi Province, China, in 1924. About 30 years ago, he came to Japan as a government student and has been living there ever since. He graduated from Kyoto University in 1948.

His family has passed the tradition of T'ai-chi Ch'uan from father to son for many generations. Now, he is a master of the Yang-style of T'ai-chi Ch'uan, teaching the simple style to many people at T'ai-chi Ch'uan Institute, Nippon Budokan, YMCA and many other places. He is also a master of the fifth grade of the Karate Institute of Japan.

He has written two Japanese books on simple style of T'ai-chi Ch'uan. This book is his latest work for beginners, and his first book in English.

QUICK & EASY SERIES

A compact and practical guide designed to be effective even with beginners. Plastic-comb-bound, the book lies flat when open, and one color photograph laminated to repel water and stain and its explanation form a double spread.

NOW AVAILABLE!

Chinese Cooking *by Constance D. Chang*
Japanese Cooking *by 15 Japanese culinary experts*
Flower Arrangement *by 12 leading Japanese masters*
Japanese Gardens *by Katsuo Saito*
Chinese Massage *by Dr. Yoshio Manaka*
Bonsai Miniatures *by Zeko Nakamura*